Billy's Coming Back

Word is out on the street,
Billy's coming back.

There's a sound outside of running feet,
somebody, somewhere's switched on the heat,
policemen are beating a swift retreat
now Billy's coming back.

Only last year when he went away
everyone heaved a sigh,
now news is out, and the neighbourhood
is set to blow sky-high.

Words are heard in the staff room,
teachers' faces deepen with gloom
can't shrug off this feeling of d
now Billy's coming back.

It was wonderful when he upp
a carnival feeling straightaway
no looking over shoulders,
each day was a holiday.

And now like a bomb, no one dares to defuse,
time ticks on while kids quake in their shoes,
no winners here, you can only lose,
now Billy's coming back.

It's dog eat dog on the street tonight,
it's cat and mouse, Billy's looking for a fight,
so take my advice, keep well out of sight
now Billy's coming back.

The Bully

The bully was always waiting,
down the lane by the big tree,
or further along at the churchyard gate.

He was someone to steer clear of,
something to avoid, if you could,
like a bad smell from a blocked drain.

He was big for his age,
bulky, ugly as a piranha:
one scowl could strip you to the bone.

Most times he wanted sweets,
some days money,
money made him smile,
money meant you were alright,
safe, for a while.

Once he twisted my arm
so far behind my back
I thought it would snap.

I closed my eyes and screamed inside.
If you let him know it hurt you
he'd do it all the more.

That was when I had no money to give
and I'd eaten my sweets,
but he must have smelt
the chocolate on my breath.

Then the postman came by
and heard the commotion.

'Alright lad' he said,
'Let him go.'
I rubbed my arm.
'That lad's bad,' he said.
I didn't need telling!

The next time no one saved me.
I shouted and waved my free arm
but it HURT, it hurt like mad,
all day, and all the next day too.
There had to be something I could do.

Dad would have said,
'Fight your own battles.'
Mum was too busy to notice:
'I broke an arm today Mum,'
'Oh lovely,' she'd say absent-mindedly,
'You must have worked hard,
now where are my pickling jars?'

Robin Hood wouldn't have stood for it.
He'd have rounded up Little John
and Will Scarlet and let the bully have it.

So I talked to Beryl,
Beryl who helped out on dangerous missions
for a packet of salt and vinegar
or a bag of potato sticks.

She said she could fix him.
It would cost of course,
these things always did.
Hitwomen come expensive.

When he caught me that night
on the road home,
I knew he'd got it coming -
I almost told him.

Next morning Beryl tipped him up
in the mud at the side of the road.
She, and the flying squad she controlled,
ran to school with his trousers.

In the playground we wound down
the Union Jack that flapped
at the top of our flag pole,
then tied his trousers to the wire
and raised them, high as we could.

When the bully appeared he was crying,
he was actually crying
and for one brief awful moment
I almost felt sorry for him.

We wound down his trousers
and handed them back.
He didn't say anything,
just wiped his face
with the flat of his hand
and took them away.

Later that day he found me
in a spot just short of home.
He stood at some distance
and scowled 'I'll get you,'
he spat, 'I'll make you pay,
if it takes all year,
if it takes....'

'And we'll get you too,'
I blurted out,
'We'll pay you back
in a different way.'

He spat again
just missing my feet,
then turned and stomped off
down our street.

Invasion

You've seen the beast from the Black Lagoon,
you've seen Dracula feasting on blood.
You've heard of the Thing from Outer Space
and the horror that crawls from the mud.

Well, this is a film you won't want to miss,
it will lift you as high as the moon.
This is a film that will thrill you to death,
at a cinema near you soon.

It's the sort of film that will make your heart
hammer away till it's ready to burst
right out of your chest, as you tremble with fear.
Sit back in your seat and prepare for the worst,

it's....

INVASION OF THE DINNER LADIES (Part One)

The Overtaker

(Fast and furious!)

I'm an overtaker,
straight down the line,
I don't hang about,
I haven't got time.

I'm an overtaker,
I can't stay back,
out in front,
ahead of the pack.

Better keep clear
in the swimming bath,
everybody
out of my path.

I'm an overtaker,
watch me run,
every sports day,
sound of the gun.

There I go,
off down the track,
nothing is going
to hold me back.

If there's a record
I'm out to beat it,
record breakers
watch me defeat it.

Head in the clouds,
I don't look round,
keep my feet
clear of the ground.

I'm an overtaker,
any old race,
in a talking contest
I'd be in first place.

Run to school,
scoot home at night,
any distance
that's alright.

Hundred metres,
second to none,
I'm an overtaker,
watch me r...............un!

Romance

I know there's something going on
between Mr Phipps and Miss White.
I've seen them in the car park,
how they linger when they say goodnight.

I caught them once in the TV room
with all of the blinds drawn down.
He said that he'd lost his glasses,
I bet they were fooling around.

When she wafts into our classroom
and catches him by surprise,
nothing is too much trouble,
there's a faraway look in his eyes.

Quite what she sees in him,
none of us really knows:
she's quite fashion conscious,
he wears some terrible clothes.

We think he sends her notes:
Please tick if you really love me,
and if she's slow to reply
we've seen him get awfully angry.

But when they're lovey-dovey,
he's just like a little boy,
cracking jokes and smiling again,
filling our class with his joy.

The Mystery Walk

Tomorrow, Year 6, as part
of your week of activities,
we're going to take you all
on a mystery walk.

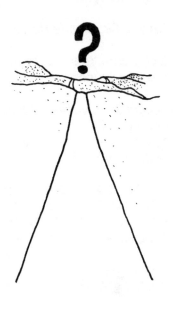

Where are we going Sir?

Well, it wouldn't be a mystery
if I told you Barry, would it?

*But my Mum likes to know
where I am Sir.*

Actually I don't know either,
I'm as much in the dark as you are.

*Oh come on Sir, you planned it,
you must know.*

Correction Barry, Mr Winters planned it.

*Oh well, in that case it will be a mystery.
He can't even find his way to the right classroom
and he's been here twenty years....*

As I was saying, or trying to say,
you will all assemble here tomorrow
at 9 O'clock.

What if it rains Sir?

You'll get wet Barry,
W E T, wet.

*But my Mum doesn't like me getting wet Sir,
I catch cold easily,
I'll be off school....*

Well, let us all hope for rai....a fine day,
alright Barry, may I continue?

Oh yes Sir, please do Sir.

Make sure Year 6 that you bring
a packed lunch....

Salami sandwiches. I love salami sandwiches,
don't you Sir?
Salami sandwiches with mustard, or pickle,
pickle's nice Sir....

I DON'T CARE WHAT YOU BRING BARRY.
YOU CAN BRING A WHOLE STRING OF SALAMI SAUSAGES,
HALF A DOZEN WATERMELONS,
A HUNDRED ICED BUNS
AND TEN GALLONS OF FIZZY DRINK,
THEN STUFF YOURSELF SILLY....
JUST BE QUIET AND LET ME CONTINUE.

When the coach drops you off
you'll be given an envelope
with instructions for finding your way home.

What if we don't get home before dark Sir?
My Mum....

I know Barry, she doesn't like you being out after dark.

That's right Sir.

Don't worry Barry, we'll find you long before dark.

So you do know where we're going Sir.
I knew it, he does know where we're going,
you can't trust teachers,
they say one thing and mean another.

Have you quite finished Barry?

Yes Sir.

Right, take a walk Barry.

Now Sir?

Right now Barry, and Barry....

Yes Sir.

This time I do know where you're going.

Where's that Sir?

To the Headteacher Barry, I've had enough.

But Sir......my Mum doesn't like me going to the Headteacher!!!

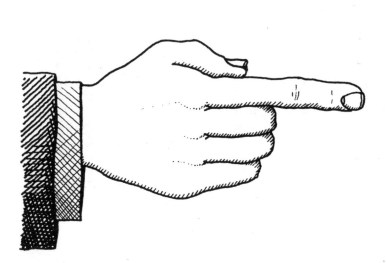

Don't Be Such a ....

Don't be such a fusspot,
an always-in-a-rushpot.

Don't be such a weepypot
a sneak-to-mum-and-be-a-creepypot.

Don't be such a muddlepot,
a double-dose-of-troublepot.

Don't be such a wigglepot,
a sit-on-your-seat-don't-squigglepot.

Don't be such a muckypot,
a pick-up-slugs-and-be-yuckypot.

Don't be such a sleepypot,
a beneath-the-bedclothes-peepypot.

Don't be such a fiddlepot,
a mess-about-and-meddlepot.

Don't be such a bossypot,
a saucypot, a gigglepot,
Don't be such a lazypot,
a nigglepot, a slackpot.

And don't call me a crackpot....
Who do you think you are?

A Liquid Waste Disposal Lorry Driver Rap

I don't want to sail a steamship
or navigate a plane,
I don't want to be a guide
taking package tours to Spain,
I don't want to be a pop star
with my fifteen minutes of fame,

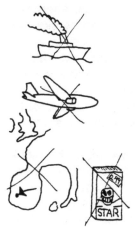

just a liquid waste disposal lorry driver.
Not an astronaut or a deep sea diver,
not a highly qualified medic
testing samples of saliva,
just a liquid waste disposal lorry driver.

When I'm up in the cab I know there's nothing
to touch my sense of fun,
several tons of liquid waste
on a long cross country run,
John O' Groats to Plymouth,
or Cork to Orpington,

I'm a liquid waste disposal lorry driver.
Not an astronaut or a deep sea diver,
not a highly qualified medic
testing samples of saliva,
just a liquid waste disposal lorry driver.

The Stuck-on-the-A1 Party

On a sunny afternoon near Barnsley
we're side by side by side
by side by side
in the biggest traffic jam
since I don't know when,
and the guy in the car next door
leans out and shouts:
'Let's have a stuck-on-the-A1 party!'

So we fetch the picnic baskets
and the bottles of pop.
We get really friendly
and play silly games,
like 'Guess when the traffic
will start up again!'

We play 'Postman's Knock'
and this huge French lorry driver kisses Mum
and looks as if he'd like to do it again
till Dad says, 'Watch it chum!'

And a guy in a van selling novelty goods
hands out party hats, balloons
and those things that you blow
to make a rude noise.

And caterers, off to some wedding,
pass round the vol-au-vents and the chicken drumsticks.
'We'll never make it now,' they say.

We swap addresses with people
from the car in front,
'If you're ever up this way again,
look us up....'

And then when a shout comes
to say we're moving on,
everyone says what a great time they've had,
and couldn't we do it again sometime?

And I'm thinking that maybe they'll really catch on,
these A1 parties - they're really fun!

Things We Did in Scotland

Had high tea in Dalwhinnie,
rowed a boat upon Loch Linnie.

Watched the fishermen in Buckie,
went skiing near Glenduckie.

Bought a tiny tartan hankie
in a shop in Killiecrankie.

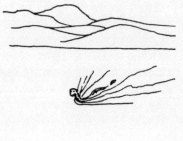

Took a walk near Inverdruie,
heard the pipes and drums in Muie.

Ate haggis in Dalmally,
saw eagles near Dowally.

Watched Highland Games in Braemar,
took presents home from Stranraer.

Thought we were in heaven
when we got to Kinlochleven,

and in Auchtermuchty town,
we watched the sun go down.

But we didn't see the monster
in Loch Ness,

no, we didn't see the monster
in Loch Ness.

Monster Crazy

Everyone here has gone Monster Crazy,
even those who are normally lazy,
binoculars raised, though the view may be hazy,
everyone here has gone Monster Crazy.

So come on Nessie, give us a wave,
don't stay hidden in your underwater cave.
You're the talk of the town, the darling of the press,
it wouldn't be summer without you in Loch Ness.

Just come on up and prove that you're there,
sometime or other you must surface for air,
somebody's camera will photograph you,
proving, at last, if you're one hump or two!

Everyone here has gone Monster Crazy,
even those who are normally lazy,
binoculars raised, though the view may be hazy,
everyone here has gone Monster Crazy.

Just waggle your flipper or flip your tail,
make some fisherman's face turn pale
as you lift your head to look at the view,
there are hundreds waiting to interview you.

Just one word Nessie, go on be a pet,
can't you stop playing hard to get?
You could be on TV, you'd have lots of money,
with American tourists calling you 'Honey!'

Everyone here has gone Monster Crazy,
even those who are normally lazy,
binoculars raised, though the view may be hazy,
everyone here has gone MONSTER CRAZY!

The 'Make Friends With a Tree' Rap

Give a tree a squeeze,
give a tree a hug,
join in celebration
with every bird and bug,

with every bat and badger,
with beetles and with bees,
a new year's resolution
for nineteen ninety-three....

Make friends with a tree,
just make friends with a tree,
hug a tree, go on show it
you really care, let a tree know it.
Make friends with a tree,
just make friends with a tree.

Trees are always homes
to every sort of creature.
In a flat and empty landscape
a tree is a special feature.

Trees can be deciduous,
pine trees are coniferous,
but trees will never hurt you
no tree is carnivorous!

So treat a tree politely,
show it you're sincere.
Long after we have disappeared,
trees will still be here.

Make friends with a tree,
just make friends with a tree,
hug a tree, go on show it
you really care, let a tree know it.
Make friends with a tree,
just make friends with a tree.

Snuggle up to a sycamore,
cuddle up to a pine
wrap your arms around an oak,
enjoy a joke with a lime.

A tree will always listen,
tell your troubles to a tree.
To the mystery of life
an ash may hold the key.

So don't be abrupt with a birch,
don't try to needle a pine.
Don't interrupt a horse chestnut,
don't give a tree a hard time.

Make friends with a tree,
just make friends with a tree,
hug a tree, go on show it
you really care, let a tree know it.
Make friends with a tree,
just make friends with a tree.

A tree is a living thing,
it's not just a lump of wood.
Trees in Sherwood Forest
know all about Robin Hood.

A tree can tell us stories,
a tree knows history,
so in this world of fake and sham
let's celebrate truth in a tree.

Make friends with a tree,
just make friends with a tree,
hug a tree, go on show it
you really care, let a tree know it.
Make friends with a tree,
just make friends with a tree.

My Brother Said

My brother said, 'I'll flatten you,
I'll tip you off your feet,
I'll push your teeth to the back of your head,
I'll knock you from here to next week.
I'll marmalise you, I'll exterminate you,
I'll change the shape of your face,
when I've finished, you won't even look
as if you belong to the human race!
I'll really give you a hiding,
I'll clobber you, I'll make you wail.
I'm going to make you regret it,
your face will turn really pale.
I'll hammer you, I'll rattle your bones,
I'll fill you full of dread.'
And I only told his girlfriend
that he still takes his teddy to bed!

Peasy!

You want me to do that ten figure sum,
        that's peasy!
Wind my legs over that bar,
slide down into a forward roll
with a double back flip to follow,
        that's peasy!
Build a working model of Big Ben
from Technical Lego,
        huh, peasy!
Clear that five foot hurdle in one leap,
cross country run up a mountain peak,
keep writing a story for one whole week,
        peeeeeeeeeasy!
Score thirty goals in record time,
in ten minutes write a thousand lines,
say *Supercalifragilisticexpialidocious* two hundred times,
        backwards.
        Oh, that's far too peasy!
BUT....
Eat the skin off of custard.
Ugh! That's the toughest thing in the world.

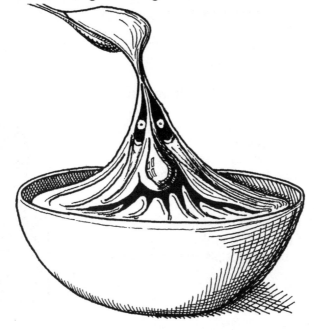

Whoppers

'We've got a pylon at the end of our garden.'

'Oh that's nothing,
we've got a gasometer.'

'Oh yeah, well we've got
a weather research station
that's manned by the Russians.'

'You haven't!'

He hadn't.

So we bashed him!

Graham was always wanting to get one better.
We all knew they were tall stories,
the kind you read in some Sunday papers:
Aliens stole my underpants
or **Baby Nessies discovered in garden pond.**

But he never tired of telling them,
no matter what,
no matter how much we yelled or thrashed him,
he'd come back for more.

Daft really, you'd think he'd have learnt.

Like after the hurricane
with everyone saying,
'A tree blew down in my garden.'
or 'We've lost the roof of our shed.'

Graham had to go and say
he'd half his house missing,
and when we took a look
there were only a couple of slates come down.

I don't know why he did it,
he knew he'd be found out,
told off, walloped.

He knew the story about the boy who cried 'Wolf'
but nothing made any difference.

He'd tell stories about his dad too,
where he worked, what he did.

My dad's a stuntman, he'd tell us,
or my dad's shooting bears in Alaska

or training to fly on the next space shuttle.

But when his dad left home,
Graham didn't say anything.

Danielle's Dragon

Danielle was sure
she'd seen dragon's breath,
out beyond the headland.

'There's a cave in the next bay,' she said.
'That's where she'll have her lair.'

We said we'd go and look,
but I knew before we set out
we'd be chasing wild geese.

Just like our trip to the rainbow's end
or the afternoon we'd dug in the yard,
thinking we'd reach Australia.

But Danielle was able to make us believe
we'd seen what she'd seen,
and that what she said was gospel,
cross-your-heart talk.

So we trudged where the tide was out,
picking up this and that on the way,
till we rounded the headland and there
in the bay was some old tramp
with a bonfire, and smoke curling into the sky.

He was boiling something yuk in a can
and he called 'Come on lassies,
there's plenty for all!'

But we took one look at
his gap-toothed grin, and his baked-bean cans
with the liquid in,
and we turned and ran as fast as we could,

as if dragon's breath was tagging our heels.

We couldn't have been more scared
if Danielle's dragon had really been real!

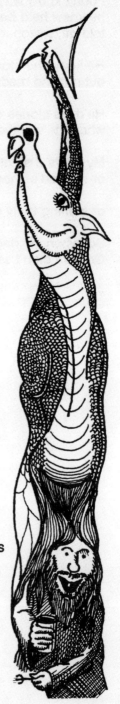

Clapping

Have you ever watched how people clap,
some of them just finger tap,
some crack palms with a mighty slap,
sounding like a thunderclap.

Shy folk only clap when they know
everyone else is set in full flow,
frightened they might end up solo,
three of four claps and then it's no go!

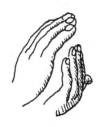

Show-offs clap above their heads
or wave their arms about instead.
Small children clap quite naturally,
when politicians clap they actually

show the side that they support,
polite applause from the Tory sort.
Labour M.P.s clap as one
brothers in rhythm everyone.

Some folk just go on all night,
right on left or left on right.
Some of them slice their hands like cymbals,
some of them spring them apart like pinballs.

Perhaps there should be schools that teach
proper clapping like proper speech,
keeping time or keeping pace
whatever the need or time or place.

Have you ever watched how people clap,
some of them just finger tap,
some crack palms with a mighty slap,
sounding like a thunder.............CLAP!

The Password

What's the Password?
I don't know.
You can't come in.
Who says so?

I say so.
You and whose army?
Tell me the password.
You must be barmy!

Just tell it me now.
What if I don't?
I'll have to fight you.
Oh no you won't.

What's the password?
I've forgotten.
Tell me the password.
You're just being rotten.

Tell me the password,
tell it to me.
Tell you the password,
oh what can it be?

Is it 'fish 'n' chips,'
is it 'Thunderbirds 3,'
is it 'Down with school,'
is it 'Open Sesame?'

I'll tell you the password,
I'll tell you it now.
The password is,
'You're a silly cow!'

That's not the password,
I'll just ignore you.
I didn't like you
from the moment I saw you.

What's the password?
See if I care.
Tell me it please,
I'm playing elsewhere.

The Puddle in Our Playground

It seems as if it's rained for weeks
and a deep puddle covers our playground.

There's something not quite right about it,
something frightening, no doubt about it.
But everyone's out there moving round it
till our caretaker says, 'Come on, get out of it,
I'll brush this clear in no time.'

But a wave rolls over the debris and muck,
the puddle give a slurp and a suck
and his broom just disappears!

'There's something queer about that puddle,
steer clear of it,' our caretaker says.

But Gavin drops his boot in, and Alison her lunch.
Well, here's a hunch, whatever's unwanted
throw it into the puddle.

Balls, homework, coats, all disappear,
'Hey, let's show teacher - bring her near,
perhaps we can give her one big push....'

'Now where's the headmaster?
Fetch him quick....'

'We've got our own Bermuda Triangle,
phone the papers, phone the TV,
it's not everyday you see
something like this....'

'Maybe if it rains and rains
and rains and rains and rains,
this puddle will swallow our school,
that'll really be cool!'

Rat Rap
(The Hamelin special!)

We're the rats,
we're the rats.

We *strut* through the kitchen and we *sniff* for cheese
We *turn* around and we *chase* our fleas.

We're the rats,
we're the rats.

We *take* the food right *out* of their hands,
we *eat* gorgonzola, it's the *best* in the land.

We're the rats,
we're the rats.

We *wake* the old men *from* their naps,
we *guzzle* the wine right *out* of the vats.

We're the rats,
we're the rats.

We *jump* into the *frying* pan,
we *grab* the food as *quick* as we can.

We're the rats,
we're the rats.

We've *kicked* the dogs right *out* of town,
they *thought* they were tops, but *we* knocked them down.

We're the rats,
we're the rats,
we're the rats,
and that's that!

(Each 'We're the rats' is followed by two beats & then four beats on a drum
or a tambour. Hit the drum or tambour again on each italicised word in the
verse.)

The Museum of Mythical Beasts

Go right in, past a beam of light
that shoots from a Cyclops' eye,
then put on armour and pick up a sword,
test how much of a hero you are:
Only the bravest & best may steal the gold
from a griffin's nest.

Then try to resist a mermaid's song.
How long will you stay before you're forced
to block your ears & turn away.

Now braver souls have tangles with trolls,
they'll carry you off to be their slave.
Careful, don't trip, just a pile of old bones,
previous visitors, I suppose!

A date with Medusa! What a surprise!
Keep your head & don't look in her eyes.
Move forward once more till you reach a door.
The Minotaur is next on our list,
a horrible task, you'd be well advised
to go prepared when you visit his lair.

That terrible smell is the Gorgon of death;
run past, run fast, don't waste any time
in escaping the blast of its breath.

Beware the Roc that will carry you off
as a titbit for one of her young
or the goblins already crouched over their pans
or the two-headed ogre who can't decide
which mouth he should pop you in!

And now you come to the final test,
a dragon, so deadly, so dreadful, so strong.
Don't weaken at all when you hear her ROAR
as you fight alongside Saint George.

Then at the exit, don't forget
to pick up your certificate,
dated and signed to say you survived
the museum of mythical beasts.

Croc City

Beneath the streets of New York
    there are sewers that stretch for miles.
They say that the sewers of New York
    are filled with crocodiles
and alligators that frightened folk
    have just flushed down the pan,
when the creatures stopped being babies
    and started snapping at their hands.

Croc City,
down below when the city sleeps,
croc city,
snapping away to a hip hop beat,
croc city.

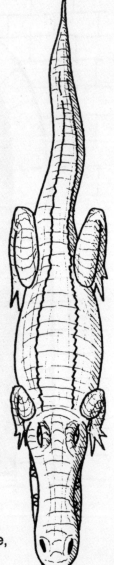

Pity the poor sewer worker
    taking his nightly stroll,
thinking about hot coffee
    at the end of his dark patrol.
Then out of the slime, a snapper
    raises its ugly head,
how fast can you sprint down a sewer pipe
    when a crocodile wants you dead....

Croc City,
down below when the city sleeps,
croc city,
snapping away to a hip hop beat,
croc city.

The State Department issue advice
    to those who find a croc,
whatever you do don't go after it,
    don't chase it with a rock.
Don't start to think you're Dundee
    out to catch a snapper.
If he opens his mouth, then you can be sure,
    this croc, *he ain't no rapper!*